First published in the UK in 2022 by Studio Press Books,
an imprint of Bonnier Books UK,
4th Floor, Victoria House, Bloomsbury Square, London WC1B 4DA
Owned by Bonnier Books,
Sveavägen 56, Stockholm, Sweden

bonnierbooks.co.uk

1 3 5 7 9 10 8 6 4 2

All rights reserved
ISBN 978-1-80078-321-8

Written by Roland Hall
Edited by Frankie Jones
Designed by Maddox Philpot
Production by Emma Kidd

MIX
Paper from
responsible sources
FSC® C018072

A CIP catalogue for this book is available from the British Library
Printed and bound in Great Britain by Clays Ltd, Elcograf S.p.A.

DISNEP
BRAIN
GAMES

FUN PUZZLES
FOR BRIGHT MINDS

STUDIO
PRESS

INTRODUCTION

Puzzles are a great source of stimulation and exercise for your brain, and they can even be fun too. Using your brain to work out a logic sequence, to calculate a sum, or to deduct the answer from a series of clues can keep you happy and occupied for hours, and it is good for you. A positive mental activity like puzzle-solving keeps your brain on its toes, so to speak! Now, if those puzzles are themed around your favourite characters from your favourite movies, that can take it to another level of fun! Heroes and villains, Princesses, animated characters and many more Disney favourites take centre stage in the wide variety of puzzles you will find in this book. There are all sorts of brain games and puzzles, from simple mathematic challenges and wordsearches to complicated logic grids and even a few taxing quizzes to test your Disney knowledge to the full!

When you start a puzzle, remember to read the instructions carefully, because sometimes there will be important rules to follow that will make the puzzle the most enjoyable it can be. And if you find yourself stuck, you can always "give a little whistle" and ask parents and carers or friends and family for help. You can even challenge your pals to a timed brain games battle!

So sharpen your pencil, calm your mind and get stuck in to this fun, stimulating series of games for your brain! Turn to the back of the book for the answers.

The Puzzles

Puzzle 1
THE MISSING NOTE

Héctor and Miguel share a passion for music, so they spend a lot of time singing and playing music together. They are rehearsing a song, but have encountered a problem – the song is missing the last note.

Find the path that connects the two singers, and discover which note is missing!

Cross off the notes in this list as you go:

C D E F G A B

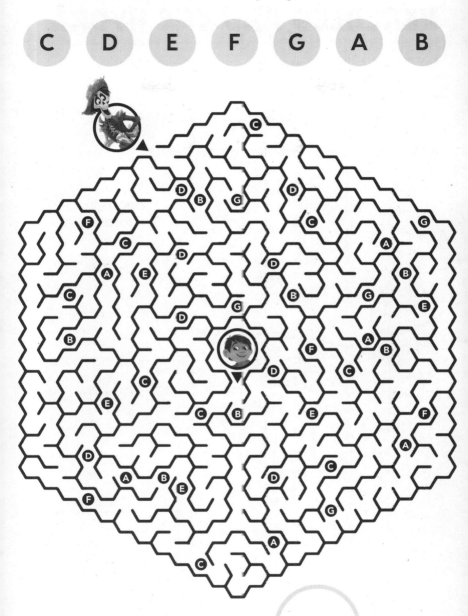

The missing note is: ....

Puzzle 2
HERCULES AND THE HYDRA

Hercules is battling the terrible monster Hydra in the cave where it dwells. At the start of the battle, Hyrdra has only one head, but each time Hercules cuts a head off, three grow in its place. He has already cut off twelve heads.

How many heads does Hydra have now?

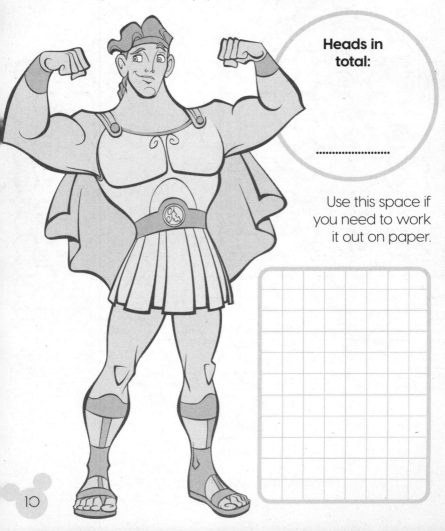

Heads in total:

....

Use this space if you need to work it out on paper.

I'M LATE, I'M LATE!

It's always "late" for the White Rabbit, and he's always checking his giant watch! Right now, it's 5:00 p.m. The White Rabbit's next appointment is in 100 hours' time but he is already worried about being late!

1. How many days is it until his appointment? ....

2. What time will it be at? ....

Use this space if you need to work it out on paper.

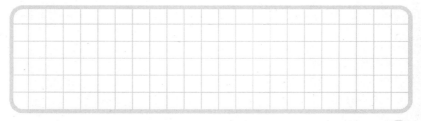

Puzzle 4
MEMORY SEQUENCE

During a test, Anger got into a fight with Fear, and that messed up Riley's memories. Luckily, Joy has a solution!

Start from memory 0 and plot the right path. Remember: each memory is equal to the sum of the two previous ones!

Use this space if you need to work it out on paper.

START

0

1

5

3

1

2

2

3

7

5

8

3

5

13

5

21

13

FINISH

13

Puzzle 5
THE GREAT RUG RACE

Woody has come up with a great idea to have fun with his toy friends: a rug race! But just after they cross the finish line, the toys hear Bonnie and they freeze.

Can you work out the order they finished in?

Bear in mind that:

Woody	**Hamm**	**Buzz**	**Rex**
finished two places before **Buzz**	finished right after **Woody**	finished two places before **Rex**	finished **last**

Use this space if you need to work it out on paper.

1ST ....

2ND ....

3RD ....

4TH ....

5TH ....

Puzzle 6
HEAD IN THE CLOUDS

Rapunzel and Eugene usually take a long walk through the streets of the kingdom, and they like to stop and look at the clouds. One day, they notice that there are clouds resembling their dearest friend, Pascal!

Count how many clouds in the sky are Pascal-shaped!

**Pascal-shaped
clouds in total:**

. . . .

Puzzle 7
A SHORT CIRCUIT!

WALL·E's language circuit got stuck, and the little robot kept repeating his name. Luckily, he managed to solve the problem. But before he did, how many times did he repeat his name?

Look for them in the grid below, and count them.

REMEMBER: The name can be written from right to left and vice versa, from bottom to top, from top to bottom, and also diagonally.

How many times is "WALLE" repeated?

Puzzle 8
MAKE A WISH

In Agrabah, many characters come into contact with the magic lamp and have the chance to be granted a wish. Can you work out who wished for what?

Use the numbers to connect each character to the right wish.

ALADDIN

....

1

To be free to choose who to love.

ABU

....

2

To become rich.

IAGO

....

3

To find a husband worthy of my daughter.

4

To have lots of food!

....

JAFAR

....

5

To become a prince and marry Jasmine.

JASMINE

....

6

To become the new sultan of Agrabah.

21

Puzzle 9
FINDING RELAXATION

Marlin is a little tired, and Dory invites him to go on holiday with her. Any destination is fine. The two friends don't have major requirements ... but there's one element that absolutely can't be missing.

Join different-shaded pieces of the puzzle to form the right word and find out what Marlin and Dory can't do without.

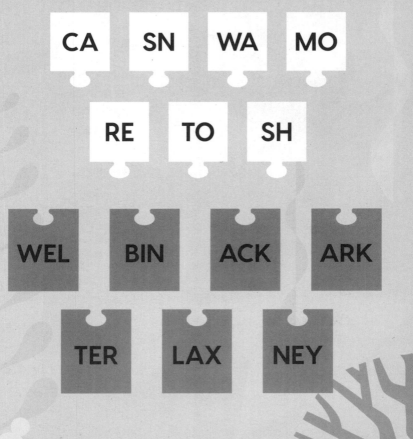

CA SN WA MO

RE TO SH

WEL BIN ACK ARK

TER LAX NEY

Use this space if you need to work it out on paper.

Puzzle 10
WI-FI AT FULL THROTTLE

Wi-Fi has been installed in the arcade to connect the games to the Internet, but it isn't active yet, because a password must be entered first.

Use logic and find the correct password, bearing in mind that it is the only word written twice in the displays below!

What's the password?

· · · · · · · · · · · · · · ·

SUGAR · FELIX · SHANK · WRECK · MULAN · ARIEL · RALPH · TIANA · GAMES · BELLE · MINTY · YES · TURBO · MA · QU · FI

FOOTPRINTS IN THE SAND

On a beautiful sunny day Moana is playing a game on the beach with Heihei and Pua.

Can you complete the sequences in the grid with the footprints, bearing in mind that no row, column or diagonal can contain four consecutive matching footprints? There are two possible solutions!

Puzzle 12
WORDSEARCH

Find the hidden pasta names in the grid. They can be hidden horizontally, vertically or diagonally, and can read from right to left or from left to right.

CANNELLONI   **FARFALLE**   **FUSILLI**

GNOCCHI   **LASAGNE**   **LINGUINE**

MACARONI   **PAPPARDELLE**   **PENNE**

SPAGHETTI   **TAGLIATELLE**   **TORTELLINI**

```
C I R I N O R A C A M T F I U
A A L I N G U I N E O U N I P
P E N L A O S I N R S I M E E
E I L N T D L G T I L L N L L
E S T L E I A L L L A L E I L
C B O C E S T L E P F A N N A
S F R A A D A T G N R F N G F
T U T L G T R N E M N A E I R
I S I E T O O A A H B A P U A
S I L A T C T C P U G F C N F
P L O R C B A A I P T A O E U
E L I H C N N G S N A I P N S
Q I I B N T P T S A E P O S I
U N E E L L E T A I L G A T L
I R P E R N O I C B N N E P I
```

Puzzle 13
THE GREAT ESCAPE

Remy, Emile and their dad Django are in the kitchen of a well-known Parisian restaurant. Unfortunately the chef doesn't like rats very much. They need to find a way out, and fast! **Help the three rats escape!**

Trace a path, bearing in mind that you always have to follow this order:

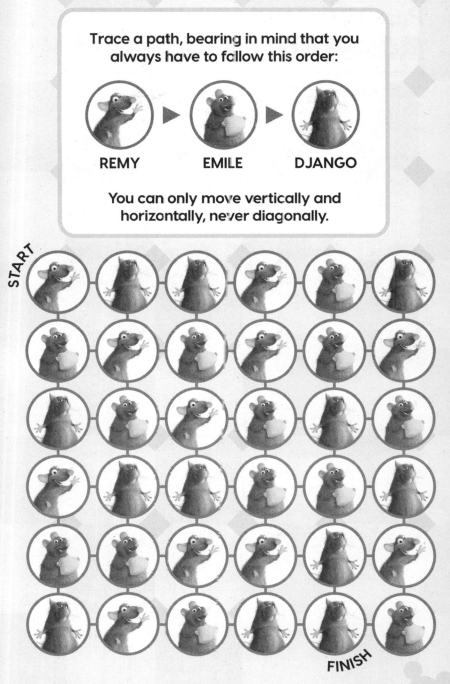

REMY ▶ EMILE ▶ DJANGO

You can only move vertically and horizontally, never diagonally.

START

FINISH

29

Puzzle 14
MONSTRO

All the whales on this page are identical apart from one.
Can you spot it?

A BERRY SPECIAL DAY

On a late summer afternoon, Pocahontas and Nakoma went in search of berries. But while they harvested them, their friends Meeko and Flit ate many berries in secret! **Read about what happened below and work out how many berries are in Pocahontas and Nakoma's basket now!**

In Pocahontas and Nakoma's basket there were **100 raspberries**.

Secretly, Meeko managed to eat **35** in a row!

Immediately after, Nakoma collected **as many raspberries as Meeko had eaten**, as well as some delicious **blueberries – 7** to be precise.

Then Meeko stole **55** raspberries and Flit stole **28**!

Eventually, Pocahontas collected a raspberry and a blueberry for every 5 raspberries Meeko stole a second time.

Berries in total:

Raspberries ....

Blueberries ....

CODEWORD

Can you crack the code to fill in the grid? Each letter of the alphabet has a number assigned to it and some are filled in for you. The words to fit into the grid are below – apart from one – **can you fill in the grid?**

3 letter words
Its
Man
Ten
Two

4 letter words
Asks
Gems
Lava
Self

5 letter words
Aging
April
Cruel
Horse
Seize
Union

7 letter words
Couldn't
Extends
Kitchen
Meeting

8 letter words
Adequate
Annoying
Finances
Hostages

10 letter words
Businesses

12 letter words
Accomplished
Increasingly

2	16	24	16		1	15	26	2	26	17	14	16
5		15		15		13		17		11		14
14	12	13	14	26	5	16		17	10	6	14	8
19		17		17			11		8			1
6		22	15	10	11	22	2	23	2	5	2	
2		14		14		11		4		26		22
13	14	26	2 A	4	10 R	15	8 L		13	20	11
14			16		16		15				16
	9	6	16	15	26	14	16	16	14	16		13
8		26		26			22		14		2
2	18	15	26	18		23	14	14	13	15	26	18
7		11		8		2		5		21		14
2	26	26	11	3	15	26	18		18	14	23	16

When it is complete the special answer word will be revealed.

1	2	3	4	5	6	7	8	9	10	11	12	13
14	15	16	17	18	19	20	21	22	23	24	25	26

Puzzle 17
BABYSITTER DORY

Dory promised Mr. Ray she'd look after his seven little pupils, but today they are nervous and often quarrelling. To avoid squabbling, Dory should split them into different sea areas, separated by seaweed. **Carefully read the rules below and find the correct distribution!**

Rules: Going from left to right, each area must contain more pupils than the previous one.

There can't be two areas with the same number of pupils.

Example: The solution to the right doesn't work. The marked area doesn't have more pupils than the previous one, and there is already another area with only one pupil.

Fill in the number of pupils in each section below.

Puzzle 18
A MOUNTAIN OF NUMBERS

Anna and Elsa are trying to reach the top of the North Mountain, but finding the right path in the deep snow isn't that easy!

Example:

Fill in the empty boxes, bearing in mind that the number in each box must be the sum of the two numbers underneath it.

Puzzle 19
LET'S MAP PETER

Captain Hook and Mr. Smee have decided to draw a map of Peter Pan's movements. They've discovered that his movements form a large square - in fact, more than one!

Look at the grid opposite and count how many squares there are.

Squares
in total:

....

Be careful: There are squares of many different sizes and each one could contain others. In the example on the right, there are five squares: four small ones and a larger one that contains them all.

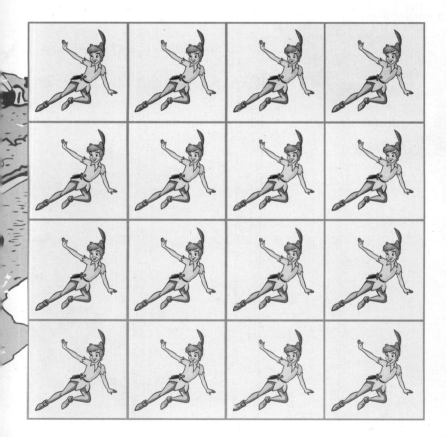

Puzzle 20
SMALL AS A FLOWER

In Wonderland, it's easy to lose all sense of scale! Right now, Alice is 20 inches tall. Find the correct sequence of calculations to bring Alice back to her normal height of 5 feet and 5 inches. **Remember there are 12 inches in a foot!**

1 Shrink Alice by 10 inches.

2 Halve Alice's height.

3 Multiply Alice's height by four.

4 Make Alice grow by 30 inches.

The right sequence is:

(...........) (...........) (...........) (...........)

Use this space if you need to work it out on paper.

TWO HEAVY SUMS

Hercules is a true hero: clever, courageous and very strong. Number each block using the six numbers on the right. The sum of the three blocks he's holding with his right hand is equal to the sum of the three blocks he's holding with his left hand. **You can do it... if you rotate your point of view!**

5

6

L

4

S

3

Use this space if you need to work it out on paper.

Puzzle 22
WORDSEARCH

Find the hidden words in the grid. They can be hidden horizontally, vertically or diagonally, and can read from right to left or from left to right.

ACHILLES   ARCHDEACON   CLOPIN   SAROUSCH

DJALI   ESMERALDA   FROLLO   TROUILLEFOU

HUGO   LAVERNE   MADELLAINE   VICTOR

PARIS   PHOEBUS   QUASIMODO   ZEPHYR

```
Y M H T R E R W Q X C R K W E
A E G N R Y M Q W X O E X E J
Z Y H A H O Z J J T Z E T O H
P G W P Z E U Q C E Q O Q O Y
T R E U F B S I L P A L U M O
N Z Q N H N V M L O P L A T U
F Q S S I L Y A E L S O S X H
S I R A P A Q C R R E R I W O
L J S R E V L O V H A F M C W
X A U O G E L L W L U L O D E
T V B U O R E W E L I G D U R
W L E S X N Z N B D K J O A R
B N O C A E D H C R A E R L Z
W Q H H Q N I P O L C M O X G
P T P B R A C H I L L E S M A
```

Puzzle 23
ALADDIN's GREAT ESCAPE

Jafar craves control of the city of Agrabah. He accuses Aladdin of a crime he never committed and orders the guards to capture him!

Carefully read the rules below and find Aladdin's route out of the city.

Rules:

The guards will arrest Aladdin if he crosses a square in their line of sight. The example in the first row of the grid indicates where the guard is looking, and the Xs show the squares Aladdin can't move through.

Move horizontally or vertically and use the buildings to hide from the guards' view.

If you can't move in front of the guards' line of sight, you can always move beside or behind them!

START

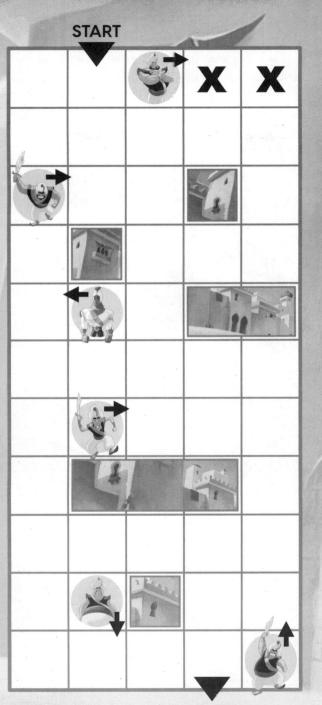

FINISH

MULAN, YES, MULAN

Mulan is playing with geometric shapes to come up with new moves for her training. At the bottom of the opposite page are the shapes she has to use to re-create each position, but in three cases Mulan changes the rule.

Look at the poses and cross out the wrong ones!

Puzzle 25
BELLE'S FRIENDLY STARS

Belle loves to look at the sky and find all the constellations. A few of them really resemble some of her dearest friends and beloved objects. Can you spot all of them?

Look carefully at the sky, connect the stars of each constellation, and then match the silhouettes to the items below!

Puzzle 26
DON'T TRAP REMY!

If Remy moves two corners in a clockwise direction and the colander moves three corners in the opposite direction, how many turns will it be before Remy is captured under the colander?

Puzzle 27
MALEFICENT

Find the shadow that belongs to Maleficent.

Correct shadow:

....

1

2

3

4

5

CODEWORD

Can you crack the code to fill in the grid? Each letter of the alphabet has a number assigned to it and some are filled in for you. The words to fit into the grid are below – apart from one – **can you fill in the grid?**

3 letter words
Any
Dye
Jar
Owl

4 letter words
Glen
Sock

5 letter words
Clove   Shelf
Clung   Table
Extra
Impel
Irons
Opera

7 letter words
Embargo
Equally
Excited
Jackpot
Lighten
Steamed

8 letter words
Auditory
Laziness

11 letter words
Christening

12 letter words
Blackcurrant
Interference

12	7	18	5		1	22	6	20	21	3	12	12
4		1		24		21		21		8		9
3	15	14	22	1	1	26		4	22	24	1	3
22		21		22			3		22			1
8	22	11	20	18	8	20	10	10	7	10		19
3				5		10		19		11		
23	26	3		18	1 L	7 O	2 V	3		7	16	1
		17		14		21		10				20
7		18	9	10	20	12	4	3	21	20	21	11
13		20		10			21		8			9
3	17	4	10	22		25	22	18	5	13	7	4
10		3		21		22		3		3		3
22	14	23	20	4	7	10	26		11	1	3	21

When it is complete the special answer word will be revealed.

1	2	3	4	5	6	7	8	9	10	11	12	13
14	15	16	17	18	19	20	21	22	23	24	25	26

LOGIC GRID

Fill in the empty boxes with the numbers 1, 2, 3, 4, 5, always following the three rules:

| A number must not appear more than once in a row. | A number must not appear more than once in a column. | A number must not appear more than once in each shaded shape. |

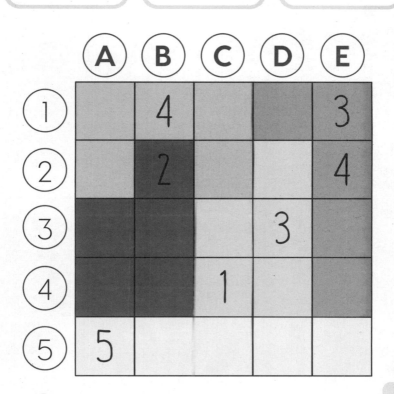

Puzzle 30
THE DEPTHS OF THE OCEAN

Marlin is swimming in the ocean with Dory. As he gradually descends into the depths, the light decreases and some fish appear only as dark shadows. **Bearing in mind that the fish lower down are all identical to those swimming higher up, how many fish does Marlin see, including Dory?**

Fish in total:

....

53

Puzzle 31
FAMOUS PHRASES

Name the characters who said the following famous phrases, as well as the movies they are in.

1. "Magic mirror on the wall, who is the fairest one of all?"

· · · · · · · · · · · ·

2. "But mother, I don't want to grow up."

· · · · · · · · · · · ·

3. "Oh my fur and whiskers! I'm late, I'm late, I'm late!"

· · · · · · · · · · · ·

4. "Am I a real boy?"

· · · · · · · · · · · ·

5. "Rob the poor to feed the rich."

· · · · · · · · · · · ·

6. "My only true love darling, I live for furs, I worship furs."

••••••••••••

7. "Before the sun sets on her sixteenth birthday, she shall prick her finger on the spindle of a spinning wheel, and die."

••••••••••••••••

8. "Remember who you are."

••••••••••••

9. "She only knows one simple fact. That you're a him and she's a her."

••••••••••••••

10. "But you see, I have the other slipper."

••••••••••••

Puzzle 32
WORDSEARCH

Find the hidden words in the grid. They can be hidden horizontally, vertically or diagonally, and can read from right to left or from left to right.

ALICE   ANITA   ARIEL   AURORA   BELLE

CINDERELLA   JASMINE   LILO   MERIDA

MULAN   MOANA   POCAHONTAS   RAPUNZEL

RAYA   RILEY   SNOW WHITE   TIANA

```
U K D N L T C O X U B J D G E
T A X T J L R A D I R E M G Z
O B N T I T N O I D A X U Z X
V Q S L A A J O R F R P N B S
N L O U O U N A V P O P H S T
Z R D M M P P A T F R N R J Q
M E G L U U O W X B U V H M X
W C B N N L C J Z Q A U A G M
Y K X Z U R A Y A S B L X F F
L E E F E S H N R H C K I N V
F L L P M U O O I F T V Q C B
X R B I C I N D E R E L L A E
I M N P R D T A L G J Y D Q L
E E A T I N A I L I S Y D L L
K F C B M Z S N O W W H I T E
```

A CUP OF TEA

After a hearty lunch, Belle wants to have a cup of tea with all the enchanted objects of the castle, but unfortunately there aren't enough cups for all of them.

Look closely at the number of cups in the boxes opposite and find out how many are missing.

> **TIP:** Pay attention to the sequence. For example, if it were: 1–6–?–16, the missing number would be 11, because we always add 5 to the previous number.

Puzzle 34
MEMORY SQUARE

This memory puzzle will challenge your powers of recall! Each number in the square corresponds to a sign, shown below.

Take 30 seconds to memorise the equivalents, then cover them up.

Next, fill in the empty square with the sign equivalents of the numbers in the first square.

$$1 = \& \quad 2 = \# \quad 3 = \% \quad 4 = /$$

1	2	4	1
2	3	1	3
1	3	2	2
4	1	2	1

Fill in the empty boxes with the numbers 1, 2 or 3, always following the three rules:

A number must not appear more than once in a row.

A number must not appear more than once in a column.

Each group of squares (shown by dotted lines) must contain only numbers that combine to equal to the number printed in the top left of the first square in the group, by using the method of calculation shown (x, +, -, ÷). For example, 3÷ can be calculated as 3 divided by 1.

Note that a number may appear more than once in a group of squares, as long as the two rules above are followed, for example:

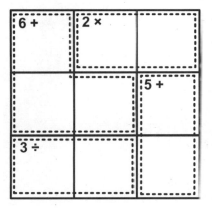

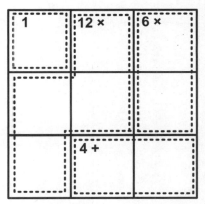

Puzzle 36
HOW A-DOOR-ABLE

Monsters, Inc. has received a supply of different types of new doors, but before they can be hung, Sulley and his colleagues need to count them all. **By doing the arithmetic, find out first how many doors of each type there are, and then how many doors there are in total.**

 +  +  = 15

 + + = 25

Use this space if you need to work it out on paper.

+ + = 23

+ + = ...

Doors in total:

..... + ... + ... = ...

Puzzle 37
THE SNOWBALL TREE

With Olaf's help, Elsa and Anna are decorating a tree made out of snowballs! Each snowball can bear one of two symbols, which must follow a precise pattern. **Look at the completed two bottom rows to work out the pattern, and draw the correct symbols on the remaining snowballs.**

Puzzle 38
SCARED!

Can you answer the questions below?

1. What is the only thing Captain Hook is afraid of?

....

2. What is Piglet scared of?

....

3. What does Dusty Crophopper suffer from?

....

4. What is the sandpiper in Piper afraid of?

....

5. What is Arlo afraid of?

....

6. What scares Winnie the Pooh?

....

Puzzle 39
ENEMIES

Can you match the baddies to the movies they are from?

1 **EVIL QUEEN**

2 **SHERE KHAN**

3 **CRUELLA**

4 **URSULA**

5 **CAPTAIN HOOK**

6 **MOTHER GOTHEL**

7 **EDGAR**

A

THE JUNGLE BOOK

B

PETER PAN

C

SNOW WHITE
AND THE
SEVEN DWARFS

D

THE LITTLE MERMAID

E

101 DALMATIANS

F

TANGLED

G

THE ARISTOCATS

Puzzle 40
REMY'S FAMOUS SOUP

Read the text below carefully once. Cover it up and then try to remember and fill in the missing words on the same text opposite.

Cut 800g of leeks into rounds and thinly slice 3 onions.

Melt some butter into a frying pan, add the leek and onion, some salt and pepper. Cook for 15 minutes, stirring from time to time.

Squeeze 3 oranges.

When the leeks and onions are cooked, pour them into a mixer with the orange juice.

Mix together and pour into a pan.

Add 50cl of water and 30cl of cream.

Cook on a medium heat, stirring frequently. Add salt and pepper to taste.

Cut .... of leeks into rounds and thinly slice .... onions.

Melt some .... into a frying pan, add the leek and onion, some salt and pepper. Cook for 15 minutes, ... from time to time.

Squeeze 3 oranges.

When the leeks and onions are .... , pour them into a .... with the orange juice.

.... together and pour into a pan.

.... 50cl of water and 30cl of ....

Cook on a medium heat, stirring frequently. Add salt and pepper to taste.

Puzzle 41
IT'S TEATIME

Tweedledee and Tweedledum told two different versions of what happened at the Mad Hatter's last tea party. But only one is right! **Read them carefully, find out who is correct and guess how many cups each guest drank!**

Bear in mind that:

- There were 4 guests.
- A total of 10 cups of tea were served.
- Everyone drank at least 1 cup.

....

MARCH HARE

....

MAD HATTER

....

ALICE

....

WHITE RABBIT

Tweedledee said that:
1. The Mad Hatter drank 3 cups of tea.
2. The White Rabbit drank 2 cups fewer than Alice.
3. The March Hare drank 1 cup of tea.

TRUE   FALSE

Tweedledum said that:
1 The White Rabbit drank 3 cups of tea.
2. The Mad Hatter drank more cups of tea than Alice.
3. Alice drank 3 cups of tea.

TRUE   FALSE

Puzzle 42
ODD ONE OUT

Which is the odd one out?

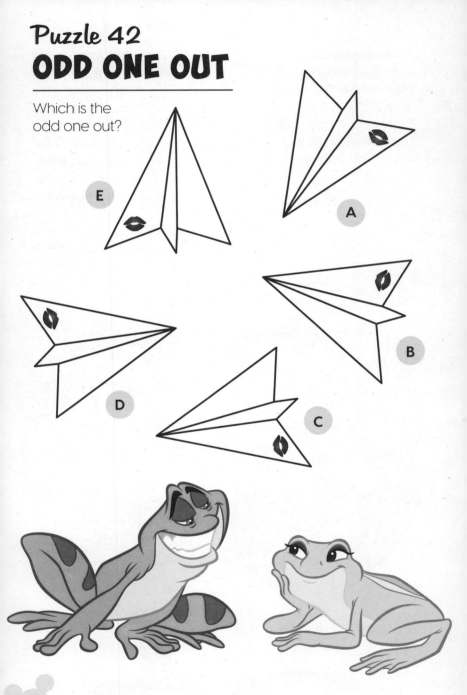

BEWARE OF THE HACKER

Randall is very jealous of Mike and Sulley's successes at Monsters, Inc. This time, to sabotage their scare session, he's changed their pass code to activate the doors. **Find the new code by doing the sums, and remember: it consists of numbers between 1 and 9 and each digit can be used only once.**

Cross off the numbers in the chart as you go:

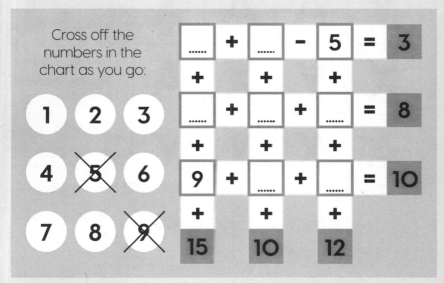

Use this space if you need to work it out on paper.

Puzzle 44
YAX

Study the grid below for 60 seconds, then cover it up. Try to fill in the blank grid with the letters from the original.

Y	A	A	X
X	Y	X	A
A	X	Y	Y

Puzzle 45
MADAM MIM'S CARDS

Using logic, can you work out the type (diamond, spade, club, heart) and the value (from 1 to 10) of the missing card?

NUMBER SQUARE

Fill in the empty boxes with the numbers 1,
2 or 3, always following the three rules:

A number must not
appear more than
once in a row.

A number must not
appear more than
once in a column.

Each group of squares (shown by dotted lines) must
contain only numbers that combine to equal the number
printed in the top left of the first square in the group, by
using the method of calculation shown (x, +, −, ÷).
For example, 3÷ can be calculated as 3 divided by 1.

Note that a number may appear more than
once in a group of squares, as long as the
two rules above are followed, for example:

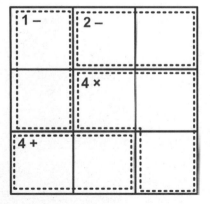

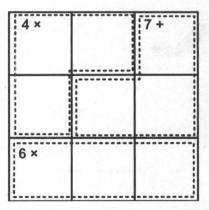

Puzzle 47
MISSING LETTERS

The vowels have been removed from the following names. Can you work out who they are? The movie they appear in is given.

SRB
(*The Lion King*)

....

MRSHMLLW
(*Frozen*)

....

MPHTRYN
(*Hercules*)

....

WNFRD
(*The Jungle Book*)

....

LSTR KR
(*Big Hero Six*)

....

MLLY DVS
(*Toy Story*)

....

FRNNY FRMGUCC
(*Meet the Robinsons*)

....

HRC BDN
(*101 Dalmatians*)

....

LOGIC GRID

Fill in the empty boxes with the numbers 1, 2, 3, 4, 5, always following the three rules:

> A number must not appear more than once in a row.

> A number must not appear more than once in a column.

> A number must not appear more than once in each shaded shape.

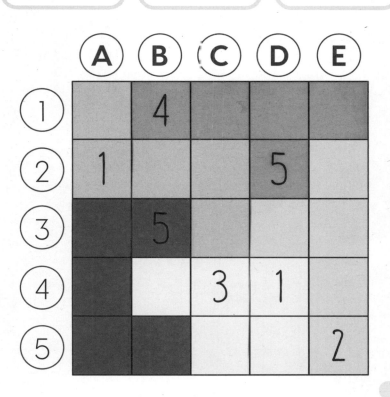

Puzzle 49
THE CORN HARVEST

Nakoma challenges Pocahontas to store four corncobs using all three baskets below ... following some hard rules. You can try too, keeping in mind that each basket can fit inside the larger ones.

Rules:

The large basket must contain twice as many cobs as the medium one.

The medium basket must contain twice as many cobs as the small one.

Pocahontas has to store all four of the cobs and can't cut them.

Write your ideas here:

ODD ONE OUT

Can you spot the odd one out?

Puzzle 51
RIDDLES ... TO MUSIC

Miguel has decided to take part in a riddle contest with a string of riddles in the form of song lyrics. Can you find the solution to each one?

1

After a big dance, back and forth, with music or without ... it always falls. **What is it?**

2

They are close to each other. They rest everywhere and they cannot see themselves. **What are they?**

3

It works hard and has learned to write but can't read.
What is it?

4

Be careful, because it has long arms but no hands. You can see the neck, but the head is not there at all.
What is it?

WINNIE THE POOH'S HONEY CAKE

Winnie the Pooh's favourite food is honey, and the ingredients for a honey cake are detailed below. **For this puzzle, study the ingredients list for one minute, then cover it up and answer the question.**

200g flour

150g sugar

1 sachet of yeast

1 pinch of salt

3 large eggs

100g butter

100g ground almonds

4 tbsp honey

1/4 litre of milk

Icing sugar

Which of the following ingredients
are not used in the recipe?

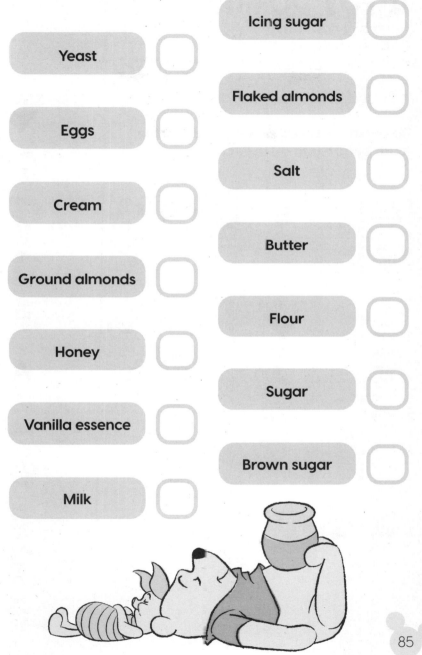

Icing sugar ☐

Yeast ☐

Flaked almonds ☐

Eggs ☐

Salt ☐

Cream ☐

Butter ☐

Ground almonds ☐

Flour ☐

Honey ☐

Sugar ☐

Vanilla essence ☐

Brown sugar ☐

Milk ☐

Puzzle 53
A TOY DOMINO

Buzz is playing a game of dominoes. Complete the path by inserting the right tiles in the empty spaces, but remember: two tiles can be in sequence only if they have the same characters at their ends.

To avoid mistakes, look carefully at the path before and after each tile.

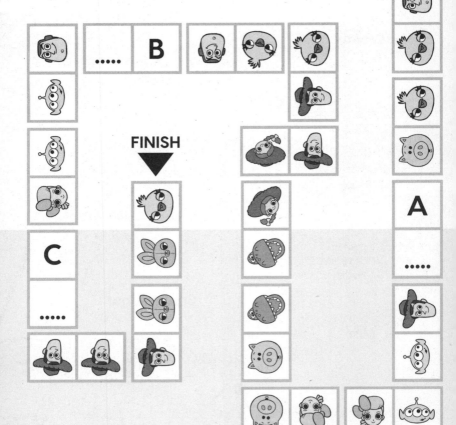

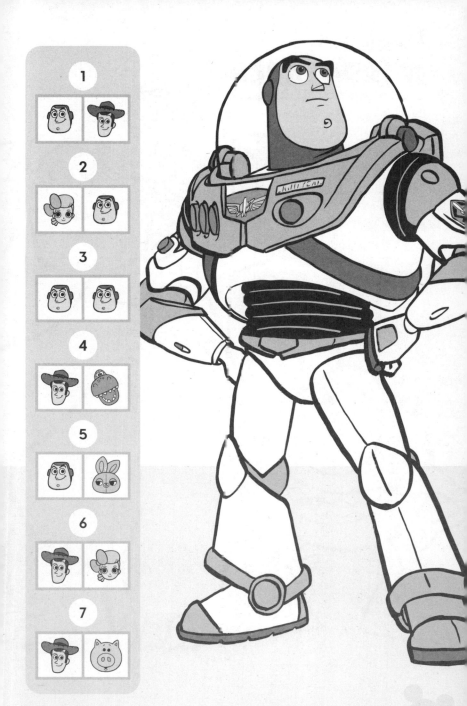

Puzzle 54
WORDSEARCH

Find the hidden words in the grid. They can be hidden horizontally, vertically or diagonally, and can read from right to left or from left to right.

BOGGS BOO BUD CELIA CHALOOBY CHARLIE

CLAWS FUNGUS GLENN LANKY MIKE

NEEDLEMAN PHLEGM RANDALL ROZ

SLUGWORTH SMITTY SPIKE STUART

SULLEY TED TONY WAZOWSKI

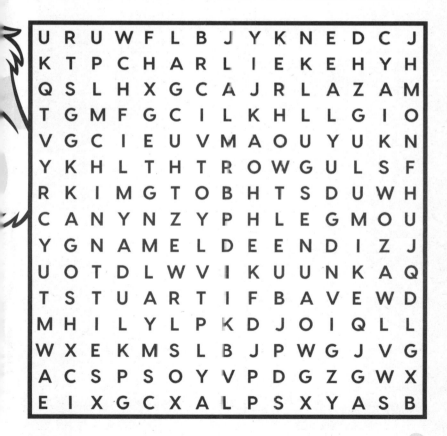

U R U W F L B J Y K N E D C J
K T P C H A R L I E K E H Y H
Q S L H X G C A J R L A Z A M
T G M F G C I L K H L L G I O
V G C I E U V M A O U Y U K N
Y K H L T H T R O W G U L S F
R K I M G T O B H T S D U W H
C A N Y N Z Y P H L E G M O U
Y G N A M E L D E E N D I Z J
U O T D L W V I K U U N K A Q
T S T U A R T I F B A V E W D
M H I L Y L P K D J O I Q L L
W X E K M S L B J P W G J V G
A C S P S O Y V P D G Z G W X
E I X G C X A L P S X Y A S B

Puzzle 55
SUPER-MESS!

Young Hercules can't control his great strength and he accidentally destroyed one of the two square decorations on the wall. Try to put the three fragments back together to make a decoration identical to the one that is still intact. **Do you think it can be done, or not? Can you explain why?**

Write your ideas here:

_____

_____

_____

_____

_____

_____

_____

_____

_____

_____

_____

_____

_____

_____

Puzzle 56
BIRDS

Link each name to the type of bird on the page opposite.

1
ARCHIMEDES
(*The Sword in the Stone*)

2
DINKY
(*The Fox and the Hound*)

3
FLIT
(*Pocahontas*)

4
HAYABUSA
(*Mulan*)

5
HEIHEI
(*Moana*)

6
IAGO
(*Aladdin*)

7
LARRY
(*Home on the Range*)

8
LUCY
(*101 Dalmatians*)

A DUCK

B HUMMINGBIRD

C COCKEREL

D FALCON

E OWL

F SPARROW

G GOOSE

H PARROT

Puzzle 57
NUMBER SQUARE

Fill in the empty boxes with the numbers
1, 2 or 3, always following the three rules:

A number must not
appear more than
once in a row.

A number must not
appear more than
once in a column.

Each group of squares (shown by dotted lines) must
contain only numbers that combine to equal the number
printed in the top left of the first square in the group,
by using the method of calculation shown (×, +, −, ÷). For
example, 3÷ can be calculated as 3 divided by 1.

Note that a number may appear more than
once in a group of squares, as long as the
two rules above are followed, for example:

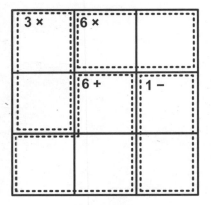

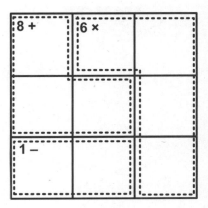

THE GENIE'S MAZE

The Genie of the Lamp is a tricky character with various expressions. **Can you find the four ways through the maze to connect each phrase with its face?**

'Say, you're a lot smaller than my last master. Either that or I'm gettin' bigger.'

'Al, I can't help you. I work for Jafar now.'

'Excuse Me? Did you rub my lamp? Did you wake me up?'

'Hang on to your turban, kid, 'cause we're gonna make you a star!'

A

B

C

D

1

2

3

4

Puzzle 59
OFF WITH THEIR HEADS

The Queen of Hearts is not known for being a hospitable ruler. On the contrary, she is very good at finding intruders and chasing them away. In each of the five groups of playing cards there is one intruder. **Can you find it, and explain why it doesn't belong?**

1 The intruder is .... because
....

2 The intruder is .... because
....

3 The intruder is .... because
....

4 The intruder is .... because
....

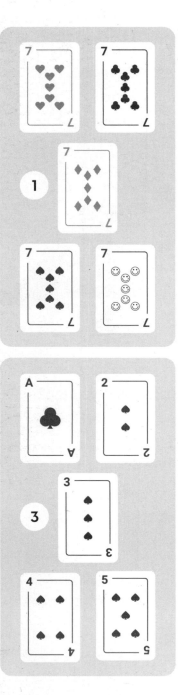

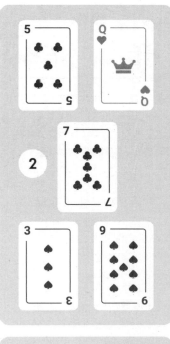

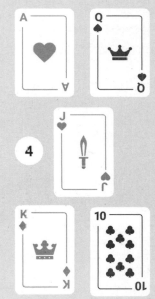

THE CASEBOOK

Judy loves making up strange crime cases and challenging Nick to solve them. **Can you help Nick figure out the two cases below?**

"The other day, two mothers and two daughters stole a rectangular painting, a square one and a round one. Although there were only three paintings, each thief took one home. How is it possible?"

Nick imagines he's a witness to the theft and immediately works out the solution – can you, too?

"Yesterday we locked up a suspect we'd been looking for for some time. Consider that he crossed the whole of Zootropolis, from one side to the other. It was a sunny day, and there were lots of people in the street, yet no one saw him. He didn't use any means of transport and no tricks. He was about to escape, but I figured out that he would come out of a damp, dark place."

Nick imagines he's the fugitive and again works out the solution – can you?

Puzzle 61
LOGIC GRID

Fill in the empty boxes with the numbers 1, 2, 3, 4, 5, always following the three rules:

A number must not appear more than once in a row.	A number must not appear more than once in a column.	A number must not appear more than once in each shaded shape.

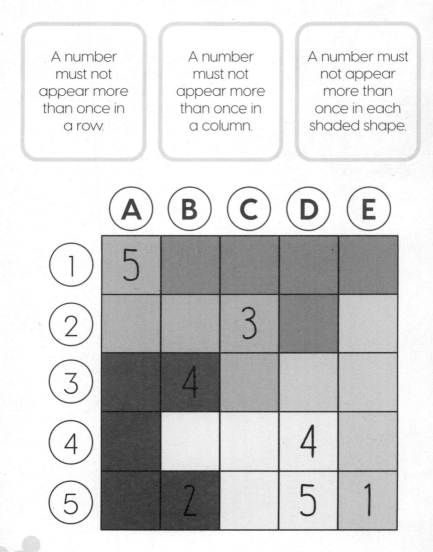

Puzzle 62
MAZE

Miguel is worried because he lost his guitar. **Can you find which two paths lead him to find it?**

1

2

3

4

5

Puzzle 63
RABBITS AND HARES

Can you match each rabbit or hare to the correct movie?

2

JUDY HOPPS

1

RABBIT

4

THE MARCH HARE

3

THE WHITE RABBIT

5

THUMPER

A
THE MANY
ADVENTURES
OF WINNIE
THE POOH

B
ALICE IN
WONDERLAND

C
BAMBI

D
ZOOTROPOLIS

103

WORDSEARCH

Find the hidden names in the grid. They can be hidden horizontally, vertically or diagonally, and can read from right to left or from left to right.

ANDY   BILLY   BOPEEP   BUZZ   DOLLY   DUCKY

GOAT   GRUFF   HAMM   HANNAH   JANIE

JINGLEJOE   LENNY   MOLLY   MONKEYS

ROBOT   ROLLERBOB   SARGE   SCUD   SHARK

SNAKE   SOLDIERS   TROLL   WHISKERS   WOODY

```
T C G S H N F T M L E N N Y F
U H U H H T L L O R T C D L Y
W Y T T O A T M L B E O U L F
I P H B O B R E L L O R C I F
X N U H G H O K Y W J R S B U
M U I D M M M A H Q E O K H R
N Y V K O S D N R Y L T A O G
E Q K E G R A S L D G N O X G
B S E C Z B R L I N N D S Y M
A Z R W U E O E X A I N Y B T
D E Y Z K D R P H L J H E J V
Q H Z S Y S X B E C O A K H Z
Z E I O H G E G Q E F D N B V
Q H Y B Y I M N P W P G O I B
W A H H G L B Q A S J D M D E
```

Puzzle 65
NUMBER SQUARE

Fill in the empty boxes with the numbers
1, 2 or 3, always following the three rules:

A number must not
appear more than
once in a row.

A number must not
appear more than
once in a column.

Each group of squares (shown by dotted lines) must
contain only numbers that combine to equal to the
number printed in the top left of the first square in the
group, by using the method of calculation shown (x, +, -, ÷).
For example, 3÷ can be calculated as 3 divided by 1.

Note that a number may appear more than
once in a group of squares, as long as the
two rules above are followed, for example:

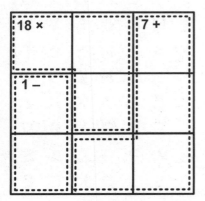

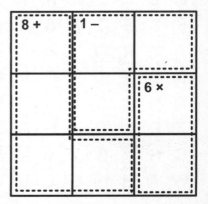

LOGIC GRID

Fill in the empty boxes with the numbers 1, 2, 3, 4, 5, always following the three rules:

| A number must not appear more than once in a row. | A number must not appear more than once in a column. | A number must not appear more than once in each shaded shape. |

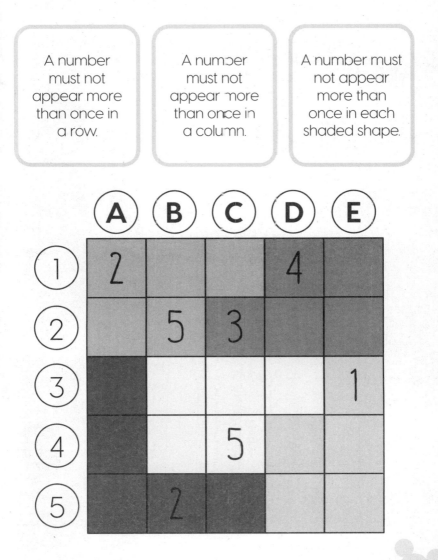

Puzzle 67
A CHECKERBOARD WALTZ

Tiana and Naveen are dancing in a hall with a chequered floor. During the dance they move 13 tiles, each time dancing horizontally or vertically, never diagonally. They never step on the same tile twice.

On which of the five framed tiles in the checkerboard below can their dance NOT end?

START

With Wall·E's he p, Eve has finally managed to reproduce some seedlings, crucial for Earth's future. Find out what route Eve took to get to the central room of the Axiom spaceship, then count how many seedlings she was able to find on the way.

START

Seedlings found:

Puzzle 69
MADAM MIM'S CARDS

Madam Mim engages in trickery of all sorts. Here she has laid out a sequence of cards that follows a pattern.

Can you work out which cards should come next?

Puzzle 70
THE PYRAMID

Dory and Marlin are counting fish in the sea and they notice a pattern.

Can you work out how many of each type of fish there should be in the box at the top of the pyramid?

White: ....

Black: ....

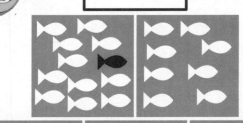

NUMBER SQUARE

Fill in the empty boxes with the numbers 1, 2 or 3, always following the three rules:

A number must not appear more than once in a row.

A number must not appear more than once in a column.

Each group of squares (shown by dotted lines) must contain only numbers that combine to equal to the number printed in the top left of the first square in the group, by using the method of calculation shown (×, +, −, ÷). For example, 3÷ can be calculated as 3 divided by 1.

Note that a number may appear more than once in a group of squares, as long as the two rules above are followed, for example:

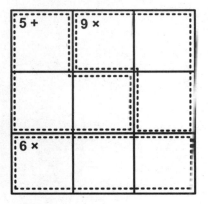

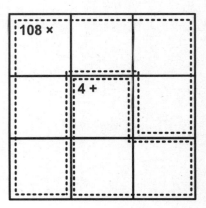

Puzzle 72
MUSIC MISSING WORDS

The list of music from *Fantasia 2000* has been muddled up and a number of words are missing. Fortunately, they are listed on the opposite page. **Can you match the word to the correct music?**

1

THE

....

OF THE ANIMALS
by Camille Saint-Saëns

2

THE SORCERER'S

....

by Paul Dukas

3

NIGHT ON

....

MOUNTAIN
by Modest Mussorgsky

4

THE

....

by Igor Stravinsky

5

PINES OF

....

by Ottorino Respighi

6

RHAPSODY IN

....

by George Gershwin

7

POMP AND

....

by Edward Elgar

A CIRCUMSTANCE

B CARNIVAL

D BLUE

C APPRENTICE

E ROME

F FIREBIRD

G BALD

Puzzle 73
BERLIOZ AND TOULOUSE

Berlioz 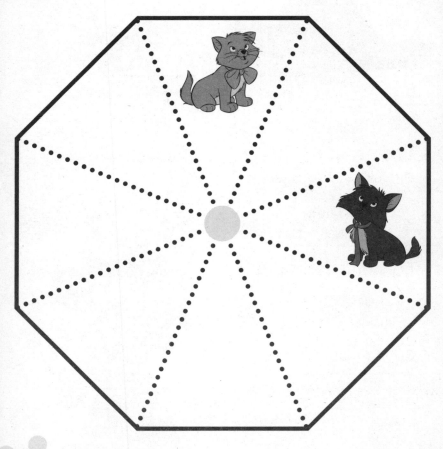 and Toulouse are playing a game of catch, but with some special rules.

Can you work out how many turns it will take before Berlioz *catches* Toulouse, if Berlioz advances 3 segments clockwise each turn and Toulouse advances 2 segments clockwise each turn?

Can you match each bear to the correct movie?

A

C

B

D

1 Brave

....

2 Toy Story 3

....

3 The Jungle Book

....

4 Brother Bear

....

Puzzle 75
BEWARE OF THE POTIONS

Ursula has prepared two potions that change Ariel's moods. Each bottle is filled with a different potion. Rotate them following the instructions to find out which potion each one contains.

SADNESS	FEAR	JOY
SURPRISE		DISGUST
JOY	ANGER	SADNESS

- Rotate 90° clockwise
- 90° clockwise
- 3 times 90° anticlockwise
- 45° anticlockwise
- 90° clockwise
- 45° clockwise
- 45° clockwise

POTION 1
contains

••••••••••••••••

SURPRISE	FEAR	SADNESS
JOY		DISGUST
SADNESS	ANGER	SURPRISE

- Rotate 90° clockwise
- 90° clockwise
- 3 times 90° anticlockwise
- 45° anticlockwise
- 90° clockwise
- 45° clockwise
- 45° clockwise

POTION 2
contains

••••••••••••••••

119

Puzzle 76
MAZE

Dory's parents left a shell trail on the ocean floor to help Dory find the way home. But a mischievous fish stole four of them, and Dory doesn't know which way to go! **Put the four missing shells back in their places and recreate the path.**

Rules: Each shell must be connected to another one horizontally or vertically.

You can't place two missing shells in two adjacent boxes.

Cross off the shells as you place them.

NEXT

What image should replace the question mark to continue
this sequence involving Rapunzel, Flynn Rider and Pascal?
Draw the answer in the boxes below.

Puzzle 78
SEA CREATURES

Can you identify each of these sea creatures by name?

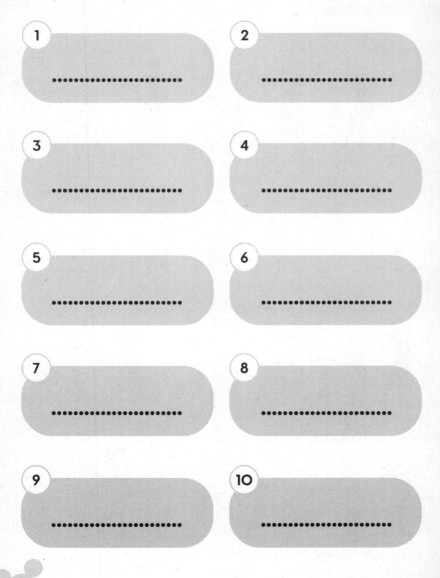

1 ....

2 ....

3 ....

4 ....

5 ....

6 ....

7 ....

8 ....

9 ....

10 ....

123

Puzzle 79
THE WAY TO SCHOOL

There are plenty of creatures and objects to see on the way to school in the Savannah, if you are observant. To solve this puzzle, first study the route to school below for one minute, then cover it up and answer the question below.

Which page from the notebook has the correct order of what you would see going from home to school?

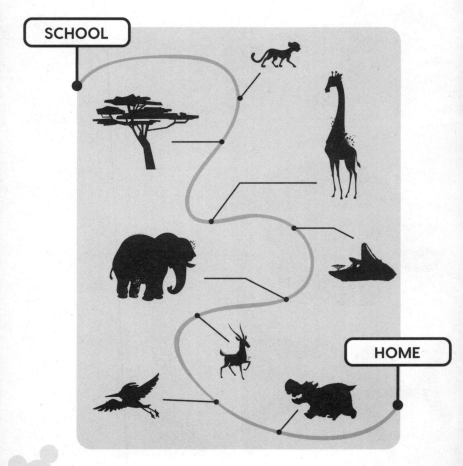

1

- Hippopotamus
- Bird
- Antelope
- Elephant
- Giraffe
- Mountain
- Tree
- Lion cub

2

- Hippopotamus
- Lion cub
- Antelope
- Elephant
- Giraffe
- Mountain
- Tree
- Bird

3

- Hippopotamus
- Bird
- Antelope
- Elephant
- Mountain
- Giraffe
- Tree
- Lion cub

4

- Lion cub
- Hippopotamus
- Bird
- Antelope
- Elephant
- Mountain
- Giraffe
- Tree

NUMBER SQUARE

Fill in the empty boxes with the numbers 1, 2 or 3, always following the three rules:

> A number must not appear more than once in a row.

> A number must not appear more than once in a column.

Each group of squares (shown by dotted lines) must contain only numbers that combine to equal the number printed in the top left of the first square in the group, by using the method of calculation shown (×, +, −, ÷). For example, 3÷ can be calculated as 3 divided by 1.

Note that a number may appear more than once in a group of squares, as long as the two rules above are followed, for example:

8 +			8 +	
4	2		2	3
2			3	

6 +		12 ×	
1 −	3 ÷		
		2 −	6 ×
4 ÷			

JAQ AND LUCIFER

Lucifer  **is trying to catch Jaq**

Can you work out how many turns it will take
before Lucifer catches Jaq, if Lucifer advances
3 segments clockwise each turn and Jaq goes
4 segments in the other direction each turn?

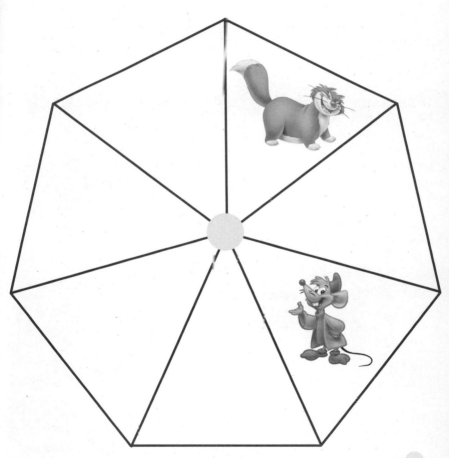

Puzzle 82
LINGUINE!

Alfredo has a recipe for pasta that he's written down, but he has left it somewhere. **Can you study the recipe for a minute, then cover it up and answer the questions on the opposite page?**

Bring a large pan full of water with a pinch of salt to the boil. Drop in 500g of linguine pasta and cook it for as long as the instructions tell you.

During that time, cut up 6 slices of parma ham and prepare the sauce: tip 30cl of single cream into a small pan with 60g of grated parmesan, the juice of half a lemon, salt and pepper. Five minutes before the pasta is cooked, heat up the mixture over a medium heat.

To finish, drain the pasta. Place it back in the pan, pour the sauce over and stir. Serve it straight away with the ham on top, and sprinkle all over with grated parmesan cheese.

How much linguine pasta does the recipe ask for?

....

What five ingredients do you use for the sauce?

....

What type of ham is used in this recipe?

....

What should you sprinkle on top before serving?

....

129

Puzzle 83
ANIMATED CLASSICS

Can you answer these questions?

1. Who assigns Jiminy Cricket as Pinocchio's conscience?
   a Geppetto
   b Stromboli
   c Honest John
   d The Blue Fairy

2. What type of bird is Zazu from *The Lion King*? ....

3. **Fill in the blank:** When Alice meets the March Hare and the Mad Hatter, they're celebrating their ....

4. How many puppies do Lady and the Tramp have?
   a None
   b 2
   c 3
   d 4

5. In *One Hundred and One Dalmatians*, what is the puppies' favourite TV show? ....

6. What is the name of the only female kitten in *The Aristocats*? ....

7. What kind of animal is Robin Hood? ....

8. Aladdin is almost always barefoot; when does he wear shoes? ....

9. Which of the following is Kuzco's catchphrase in *The Emperor's New Groove*?
   a 'Boo-yah!'
   b 'No touchy!'
   c 'Boom, baby!'
   d All of the above

10. What is the name of the train in *Dumbo*?
....

11. What can Stitch not do when he first arrives on Earth? ....

12. In *Pinocchio*, what is Geppetto's profession? ....

13. In *The Lion King*, which of Scar's eyes has a scar over it? ....

14. In *The Little Mermaid*, what does Ursula accidentally turn Flotsam and Jetsam into?
   a Sea particles
   b Dolphins
   c Crabs
   d Kelp

15. **True or false?** In *The Sword in the Stone*, Arthur's nickname is Wart. ....

Puzzle 84
NUMBER SQUARE

Fill in the empty boxes with the numbers 1, 2 or 3, always following the three rules:

A number must not appear more than once in a row.

A number must not appear more than once in a column.

Each group of squares (shown by dotted lines) must contain only numbers that combine to equal the number printed in the top left of the first square in the group, by using the method of calculation shown (×, +, −, ÷). For example, 3÷ can be calculated as 3 divided by 1.

Note that a number may appear more than once in a group of squares, as long as the two rules above are followed, for example:

2 −	3 −		3 ÷	7 +	
	1 −			10 +	
4 +		2 ÷			2 −
2 ÷	4 −		2 −		
		6 ×	24 ×		5 +
7 +			5 +		

PARENTS

Many parents, many children, many films. But can you match the parents and name the films they are from? Fill in the grid on the opposite page.

Queen Leah

Robert

Darling

George

King Stefan

Mrs Darling

Anita

Jim Dear

Roger Radcliffe

Helen

Parent 1	Parent 2	Film
1		
....	....	....
2		
....	....	....
3		
....	................▪............	....
4		
....	...................▪................	....
5		
....	..................▪..................	....

Puzzle 86
DINOSAUR PRINTS

Note: size does not count as a difference.

How many different dinosaur poses are there?

Poses in total:

. . . .

MEMORY SQUARE

This memory puzzle will challenge your powers of recall! Each number in the square corresponds to a sign, shown below.

Take 30 seconds to memorise the equivalents, then cover them up.

Next, fill in the empty square opposite with the sign equivalents of the numbers in the first square.

1 = /   2 = %   3 = &   4 = >   5 = #

2	4	2	3	2
3	1	2	1	5
2	1	3	2	4
3	4	3	4	2
5	3	4	5	1

Puzzle 88
REPTILES

Can you identify
each of these reptiles
by name and do you
know which movies
they are from?

2

1

1

2

139

Puzzle 89
THE NATURAL HISTORY MUSEUM

Look at the map below for one minute, then cover it up and follow the instructions on the opposite page.

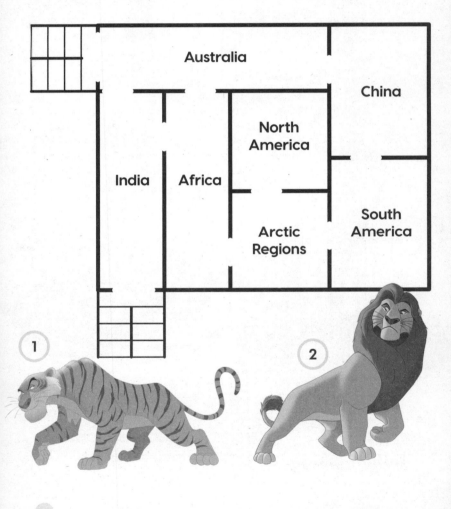

1 Fill in the map with the number of animals that belong in the correct habitat.

2 Can you name all the animals and the films they are in?

3

4

5

141

Puzzle 90
THE WORLD OF SONGS

Can you name the movie that each of these songs comes from?

1
Whistle While You Work

....

2
Everybody Wants
To Be A Cat

....

3
Can You Feel the
Love Tonight?

....

4
Colonel Hathi's March

....

5
I'm Late

....

6
We Don't Talk
About Bruno

....

7
Out There

....

8
Baby Mine

....

9
Route 66

....

10
Higitus Figitus

....

Puzzle 91
RATS AND MICE

Can you name these rats and mice
and the movies they are from?

1

2

3

4

5

6

7

Puzzle 92
MADAM MIM'S CARDS

Madam Mim engages in trickery of all sorts.
This time she has laid out a group of cards.

**Can you work out which line is
the odd one out, and why?**

The odd one out is

....

because

....

....

As a bonus,
can you name
five animals
that Madam
Mim transforms
herself into?

1 ....   2 ....

3 ....

4 ....   5 ....

Puzzle 93
MATHEMATIC SUDOKU

Fill in the grid with the numbers 1 to 9 once only in each row, column and 3x3 square.

This sudoku is divided into smaller sections, shown with a dotted outline. In each of these is shown a number that is the total of the numbers in that section. To help you, four numbers have been added already.

15	4		7		9	11	12	
	11		5	17			8	
6	11 **2**	**9**			8	8		10
	14		10			14		
7	11	13		10		9	16	7 **5**
		15	10					**2**
9			8	16		13	3	
15		3		5			11	
10			14		6		14	

LOGIC GRID

Fill in the empty boxes with the numbers 1, 2, 3, 4, 5, always following the three rules:

A number must not appear more than once in a row.	A number must not appear more than once in a column.	A number must not appear more than once in each shaded shape.

	A	B	C	D	E	F
1	5					2
2					4	
3		3		1		
4		6	4			
5	2			6	3	
6			5			3

Puzzle 95
ROBOTS

Can you match each robot with its name?

A Auto

B Baymax

C B.E.N.

D Carl

E DOR-15

F EVE

G Go-4

H M-O

I Omnidroid

J Sparks

K WALL·E

L Zurg

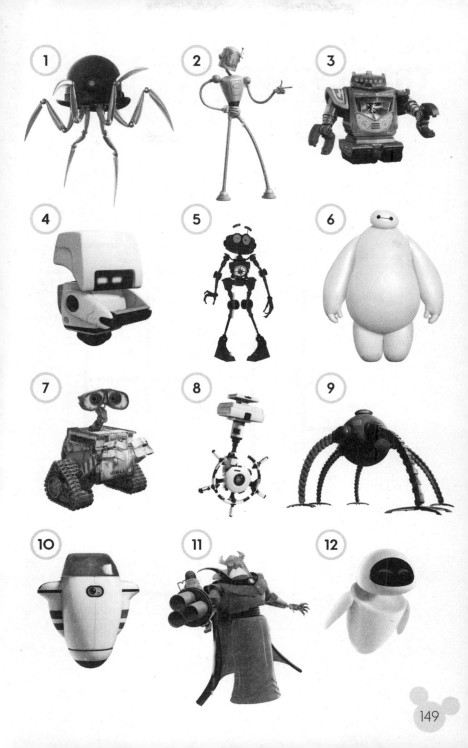

Puzzle 96
THE RESTAURANT

Study the map below for one minute, then cover it up and answer the question on the opposite page.

 = **You are here**

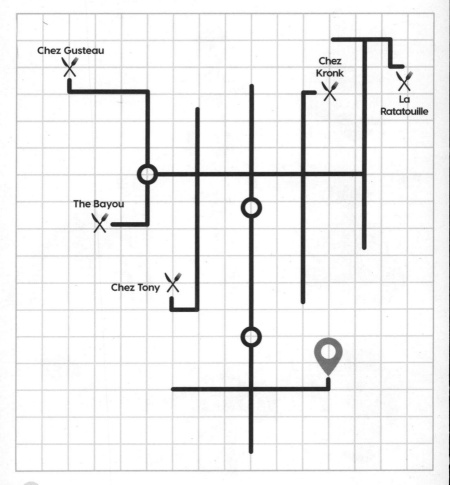

Give directions to get to the restaurant La Ratatouille. Use the space below to draw the map if you need to.

Puzzle 97
TRANSFORMATION

Can you join these people with their
(wanted or unwanted) transformations?

1
ARTHUR

2
JAFAR

3
KUZCO

4
MADAM MIM

5
MALEFICENT

6
SNOW WHITE'S STEPMOTHER

7
MERLIN

8
MOR'DU

9
PRINCE NAVEEN

10
YZMA

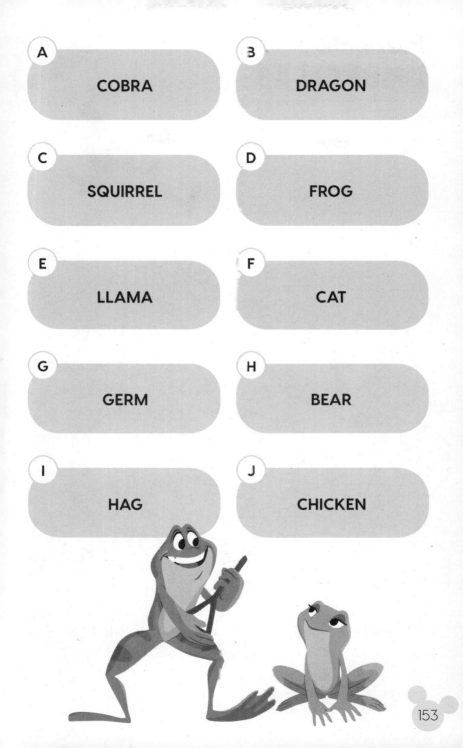

A COBRA

B DRAGON

C SQUIRREL

D FROG

E LLAMA

F CAT

G GERM

H BEAR

I HAG

J CHICKEN

Puzzle 98
UMBRELLAS

It's a blustery day and Edgar needs to hold on to his umbrella with all his might. He doesn't have the only umbrella on the page though. Can you count how many other brollies there are?

Umbrellas
in total: ....

Puzzle 99
THE SEQUENCE

Using logic, can you work out how many umbrellas are missing from the sequence, and where they should be?

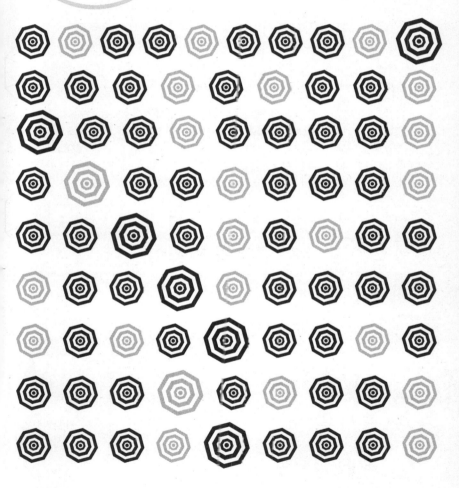

NUMBER SQUARE

Fill in the empty boxes with the numbers 1, 2 or 3, always following the three rules:

| A number must not appear more than once in a row. | A number must not appear more than once in a column. |

Each group of squares (shown by dotted lines) must contain only numbers that combine to equal to the number printed in the top left of the first square in the group, by using the method of calculation shown (x, +, -, ÷). For example, 3÷ can be calculated as 3 divided by 1.

Note that a number may appear more than once in a group of squares, as long as the two rules above are followed, for example:

1 −		4 −		3 ÷	
3 −	6 +		1 −		2 −
	6 ×	1 −	3 ÷		
3 ÷			3 −	10 ×	24 ×
	15 ×				
8 +		6 ×		6 +	

The Answers

Puzzle 1
THE MISSING NOTE
The missing note is **F**.

Puzzle 2
HERCULES AND THE HYDRA
Every time a head is cut off, three grow back, so that means two more are added to however many heads it has. Cutting off twelve heads will thus add 24. Added to the initial head, that means the Hydra has **25** heads at the moment.

Puzzle 3
I'M LATE, I'M LATE!
1. The White Rabbit's appointment is in **4** days.
2. In 100 hours it will be **9:00 p.m. (21:00)**.

Puzzle 4
MEMORY SEQUENCE

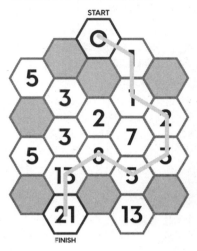

Puzzle 5
THE GREAT RUG RACE
1st: Woody
2nd: Hamm
3rd: Buzz
4th: Slinky
5th: Rex

Puzzle 6
HEAD IN THE CLOUDS
There are **8** Pascal-shaped clouds in the sky.

Puzzle 7
A SHORT CIRCUIT!
12 horizontal + 9 vertical + 4 diagonal = **25** times.

Puzzle 8
MAKE A WISH

1. To be free to choose who to love. – JASMINE
2. To become rich. – IAGO
3. To find a husband worthy of my daughter. – THE SULTAN
4. To have lots of food! – ABU
5. To become a prince and marry Jasmine. – ALADDIN
6. To become the new sultan of Agrabah. – JAFAR

Puzzle 9
FINDING RELAXATION
Given that they're two fish, Marlin and Dory need WATER.

Puzzle 10
WI-FI AT FULL THROTTLE
The password is **FELIX**. Since there are no two displays showing the same password in full, it means the right one must start with the letters that can be seen on the covered displays. None of the full words start with "MA" "Q" or "YES," while only "FELIX" starts with "F," so the two displays have the same password.

Puzzle 11
FOOTPRINTS IN THE SAND

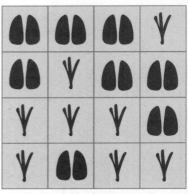

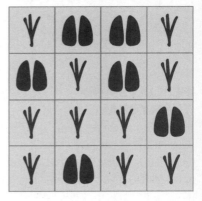

Puzzle 12
WORDSEARCH

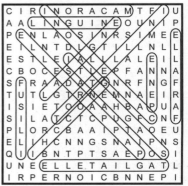

Puzzle 13
THE GREAT ESCAPE

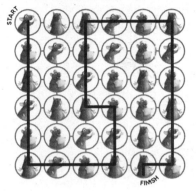

Puzzle 14
MONSTRO
Second page, sixth line, third whale from left.

Puzzle 15
A BERRY SPECIAL DAY
Pocahontas and Nakoma now have **28** raspberries and **18** blueberries.

Puzzle 16
CODEWORD
HIROHAMADA

Puzzle 17
BABYSITTER DORY
The only way to split up the pupils following the two rules is to have none in the area furthest to the left, and then respectively 1, 2 and 4 in the following areas:
0 => **1** => **2** => **4**

Puzzle 18
A MOUNTAIN OF NUMBERS

Puzzle 19
LET'S MAP PETER
There are **30** squares: one 4x4, four 3x3, nine 2x2, sixteen 1x1.

Puzzle 20
SMALL AS A FLOWER
The correct sequence is **3, 1, 2, 4**. 20x4=80; 80-10=70; 70/2=35; 35+30=65. 65 inches = 5 feet and 5 inches.

Puzzle 21
TWO HEAVY SUMS
The sum of the six blocks is 21. Since 21 is an odd number, you can't divide it exactly by two, so the task seems impossible. But if you rotate your point of view, the 6 can turn into a 9! In this way you can put 3, 4 and 5 in one hand and 1, 2

and 9 in the other.
The sum of the numbers
in each hand is then **12**.

Puzzle 22
WORDSEARCH

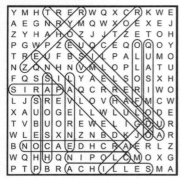

Puzzle 23
ALADDIN'S GREAT ESCAPE

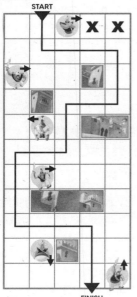

Puzzle 24
MULAN, YES, MULAN
Mulan changes the rule in
poses **1**, **6** and **8** because
she uses an extra piece!

Puzzle 25
BELLE'S FRIENDLY STARS
1 - D   2 - C   3 - A   4 - B   5 - E

Puzzle 26
DON'T TRAP REMY!
On the third turn.

Puzzle 27
MALEFICENT
3.

Puzzle 28
CODEWORD
MAGICMIRROR

Puzzle 29
LOGIC GRID

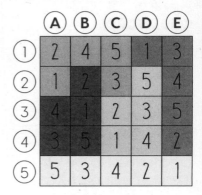

Puzzle 30
THE DEPTHS OF THE OCEAN
Marlin sees **21** fish. When counting them, pay attention to those that always swim in pairs and the three next to each other that look like one big fish, and look carefully through the seaweed!

Puzzle 31
FAMOUS PHRASES
1. The Queen in *Snow White and the Seven Dwarfs*
2. Wendy in *Peter Pan*
3. The White Rabbit in *Alice in Wonderland*
4. Pinocchio in *Pinocchio*
5. Prince John in *Robin Hood*
6. Cruella in *101 Dalmatians*
7. Maleficent in *Sleeping Beauty*
8. Mufasa in *The Lion King*
9. Merlin in *The Sword in the Stone*
10. Cinderella in *Cinderella*

Puzzle 32
WORDSEARCH

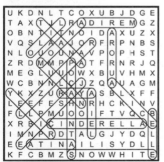

Puzzle 33
A CUP OF TEA
There are **10** missing cups: 1–4–7–10–13.

Puzzle 34
MEMORY SQUARE

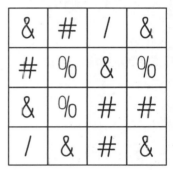

Puzzle 35
NUMBER SQUARE

163

Puzzle 36
HOW A-DOOR-ABLE

 10 + ▮ 8 + ▮ 8 = 26

There are **23** doors in total.

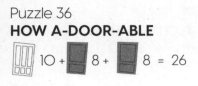 5   ▦ 10   ▮ 8

Puzzle 37
THE SNOWBALL TREE

if two snowballs contain the same symbol (two snowflakes or two crocuses), then the snowball above them contains the crocus symbol; whereas if two snowballs contain two different symbols (a snowflake and a crocus), then the snowball above them contains the snowflake symbol.

Puzzle 38
SCARED!
1. Tick-Tock the Crocodile.
2. Heffalumps and Woozles.
3. Dusty Crophopper has vertigo (fear of heights).
4. Scared of water/waves.
5. Prehistoric chickens.
6. That someone will steal his honey.

Puzzle 39
ENEMIES
1. Evil Queen – *Snow White and the Seven Dwarfs*
2. Shere Khan – *The Jungle Book*
3. Cruella – *101 Dalmatians*
4. Ursula – *The Little Mermaid*
5. Captain Hook – *Peter Pan*
6. Mother Gothel – *Tangled*
7. Edgar – *The Aristocats*

Puzzle 41
IT'S TEATIME
Tweedledum's version is false, because if the Mad Hatter drank more cups than Alice, it means that he drank at least 4; these added to Alice's 3 and the White Rabbit's 3 make 10, but then there wouldn't even be 1 cup left for the March Hare to drink. So we know that **Tweedledee's version is true**. The Hatter therefore drank 3 cups and the March Hare 1. That leaves 6 cups, and we know that the White Rabbit drank 2 fewer than Alice. Therefore,

if there are a total of 6 cups left, the only possible solution is that Alice drank 4 cups and the White Rabbit 2.
To sum up: the March Hare drank **1** cup of tea, the White Rabbit drank **2** cups, Alice drank **4** cups and the Mad Hatter drank **3** cups.

Puzzle 42
ODD ONE OUT
C. The lipstick is on the opposite wing from all the others.

Puzzle 43
BEWARE OF THE HACKER

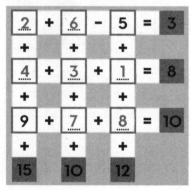

Puzzle 45
MADAM MIM'S CARDS
The **8 of Clubs**. The cards are the same suit in each column, and the value of the third card in each row is the sum of the two previous cards.

Puzzle 46
NUMBER SQUARE

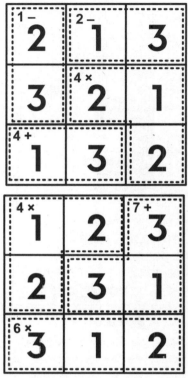

Puzzle 47
MISSING LETTERS
SARABI
ALISTAIR KREI
MARSHMALLOW
MOLLY DAVIS
AMPHITRYON
FRANNY FRAMAGUCCI
WINIFRED
HORACE BADUN

Puzzle 48
LOGIC GRID

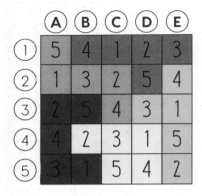

Puzzle 49
THE CORN HARVEST
Pocahontas puts one cob in the small basket, one in the medium basket, and two in the large basket. Then she puts the small basket into the medium one, and both into the large one. That way, the large basket contains all four cobs (because it also contains a cob for each basket inside it), the medium one contains two (including the one in the small basket) and the instructions are followed by having **1**, **2** and **4** cobs of corn in the baskets.

Puzzle 50
ODD ONE OUT
A. It is the only line in which Judy Hopps and Nick Wilde are separated.

Puzzle 51
RIDDLES ... TO MUSIC
1. A tooth
2. The eyes
3. A hand
4. A jumper

Puzzle 53
A TOY DOMINO
A – 7   B – 3   C – 6

Puzzle 54
WORDSEARCH

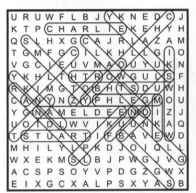

Puzzle 55
SUPER-MESS!
It is possible to re-create a square with the three fragments, but the two decorations will not be identical. The reason is that one of the pieces has to be turned to fit alongside the other, so the decoration on those tiles will be sideways compared to the others.

Puzzle 56
BIRDS
1 – E	2 – F	3 – B	4 – D
5 – C	6 – H	7 – A	8 – G

Puzzle 57
NUMBER SQUARE

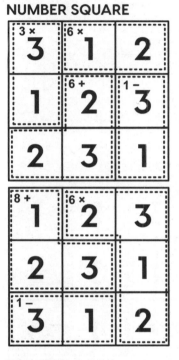

Puzzle 58
THE GENIE'S MAZE

Puzzle 59
OFF WITH THEIR HEADS

1. The intruder is the 7 smilies because the smiley isn't a playing card symbol.

2. The intruder is the Queen of Hearts because it's the only one that's not in sequence.

3. The intruder is the Ace of Clubs because it's the only non-spades card.

4. The intruder is the 10 of Clubs because it's the only card that doesn't have a letter.

Puzzle 60
THE CASEBOOK

Case 1: Because there are three thieves: a grandmother, a mother and a daughter. **The mother is, in fact, both a mother and a daughter.**
Case 2: The fugitive used **the sewer system**.

Puzzle 61
LOGIC GRID

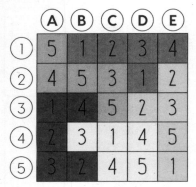

Puzzle 62
MAZE

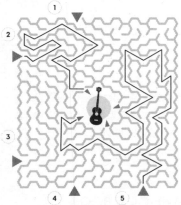

Entrances 1 and 5 lead Miguel to his guitar.

Puzzle 63
RABBITS AND HARES

A – 2   B – 4   C – 1   D – 1
E – 3

Puzzle 64
WORDSEARCH

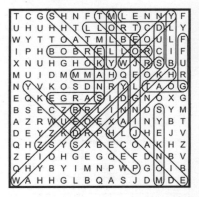

Puzzle 65
NUMBER SQUARE

Puzzle 66
LOGIC GRID

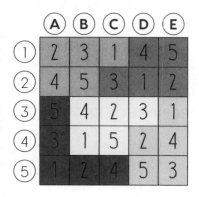

Puzzle 67
A CHECKERBOARD WALTZ

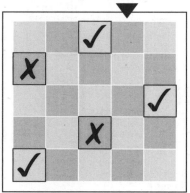

Tiana and Naveen can never stop in the two squares marked X. Starting from a tile with a dark background, after moving 13 tiles, they have to stop on a square with a light background, because the shades alternate. The other three tiles, however, can be reached in various ways following the rules given.

Puzzle 68
MAZE

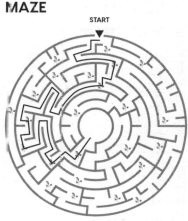

Eve found 6 seedlings.

Puzzle 69
MADAM MIM'S CARDS
The ace of diamonds and the ace of spades, so that each card appears three times.

Puzzle 70
THE PYRAMID
19 white fish and 1 black fish. In each box, the number of white fish is the total of the white fish in the two boxes below it. The number of black fish is calculated by subtracting the number of black fish in the two boxes below it.

Puzzle 71
NUMBER SQUARE

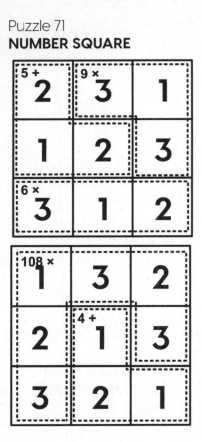

Puzzle 72
MUSIC MISSING WORDS
1 - B 2 - C 3 - G 4 - F
5 - E 6 - D 7 - A

Puzzle 73
BERLIOZ AND TOULOUSE
6 turns.

Puzzle 74
BEARS
1. C - Queen Elinor, *Brave*
2. D - Lotso, *Toy Story 3*
3. B - Baloo, *The Jungle Book*
4. A - Koda, *Brother Bear*

Puzzle 75
BEWARE OF THE POTIONS
Potion 1 contains **joy**.
Potion 2 contains **surprise**.

Puzzle 76
MAZE

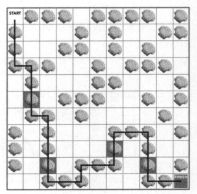

Puzzle 77
NEXT
1. Small Flynn Rider. The first 4 characters repeat.
2. Small Pascal. There are 3 small characters, then 3 large, then 3 small .
3. Small Rapunzel. There is 1 large character then 2 small.
4. 1 big Pascal. The sequence alternates

big and small images,
and the order is Flynn
Rider, Rapunzel, Pascal.

Puzzle 78
SEA CREATURES
1 – Jacques   2 – Flounder
3 – Sheldon   4 – Sebastian
5 – Pearl   6 – Bailey
7 – Crush   8 – Hank
9 – Destiny   10 – Gerald

Puzzle 79
THE WAY TO SCHOOL
3.

Puzzle 80
NUMBER SQUARE

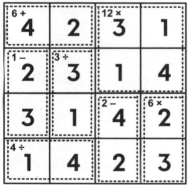

Puzzle 81
JAQ AND LUCIFER
Lucifer will never catch Jaq.
They will always remain the
same distance from each
other.

Puzzle 83
ANIMATED CLASSICS
1.   D
2.   A hornbill
3.   Unbirthdays
4.   D
5.   The Thunderbolt
Adventure Hour
6.   Marie
7.   A fox
8.   When he is Prince Ali
9.   D
10.   Casey Jr.
11.   Stitch can't swim
12.   A wood carver
13.   His left eye
14.   A
15.   True

Puzzle 84
NUMBER SQUARE

2− 4	3− 6	3	3+ 2	7+ 1	5
2	1− 4	5	6	10+ 3	1
4+ 1	3	2+ 4	5	2	2− 6
2+ 6	4− 1	2	2− 3	5	4
3	5	6× 1	24× 4	6	5+ 2
5	2	6	5× 1	4	3

Puzzle 85
PARENTS

Queen Leah and King Stefan from *Sleeping Beauty*
Robert Parr and Helen Parr from *The Incredibles*
Jim Dear and Darling from *Lady and the Tramp*
George Darling and Mrs Darling from *Peter Pan*
Anita and Roger Radcliffe from *101 Dalmatians*

Puzzle 86
DINOSAUR PRINTS

5   5   4

There are 3 poses in total.

Puzzle 87
MEMORY SQUARE

%	>	%	&	%
&	/	%	/	#
%	/	&	%	>
&	>	&	>	%
#	&	>	#	/

Puzzle 88
REPTILES

1. Pascal – *Tangled*
2. Louis – *The Princess and the Frog*
3. Tick-Tock the Crocodile – *Peter Pan*
4. Larry – *The Wild*
5. Kaa – *The Jungle Book*

Puzzle 89
THE NATURAL HISTORY MUSEUM

1. Shere Khan from *The Jungle Book* belongs in India
2. Mufasa from *The Lion King* belongs in Africa
3. Meeko from *Pocahontas* belongs in North America
4. Kuzko from *The Emperor's New Groove* belongs in South America
5. Kanga from *The Many Adventures of Winnie the Pooh* belongs in Australia

1 animal each belongs in India, Africa, North America, South America and Australia. 0 animals belong in China and the Arctic Regions.

Puzzle 90
THE WORLD OF SONGS
1. *Snow White and the Seven Dwarfs*
2. *The Aristocats*
3. *The Lion King*
4. *The Jungle Book*
5. *Alice in Wonderland*
6. *Encanto*
7. *The Hunchback of Notre Dame*
8. *Dumbo*
9. *Cars*
10. *The Sword in the Stone*

Puzzle 91
RATS AND MICE
1. Remy from *Ratatouille*
2. Jaq from *Cinderella*
3. Emile from *Ratatouille*
4. Gus from *Cinderella*
5. Mary, Perla and Suzy from *Cinderella*
6. Basil from *Basil the Great Mouse Detective*
7. Timothy Q. Mouse from *Dumbo*

Puzzle 92
MADAM MIM'S CARDS
3. The 2 of hearts is the wrong colour.
Bonus question, choose from: Pig, Cat, Crocodile, Fox, Chicken, Elephant, Tiger, Snake, Rhino, Dragon, Human.

Puzzle 93
MATHEMATIC SUDOKU

7	1	3	2	5	6	9	4	8
8	5	6	4	9	3	2	1	7
4	2	9	1	8	7	5	3	6
2	9	5	7	3	1	8	6	4
6	3	4	9	2	8	1	7	5
1	8	7	6	4	5	3	9	2
5	4	8	3	7	9	6	2	1
9	6	2	5	1	4	7	8	3
3	7	1	8	6	2	4	5	9

Puzzle 94
LOGIC GRID

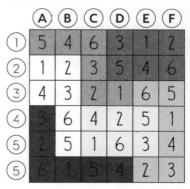

Puzzle 95
ROBOTS
1 – E   2 – D   3 – J   4 – H
5 – C   6 – B   7 – J   8 – A
9 – I   10 – G   11 – L   12 – F

Puzzle 97
TRANSFORMATION
1 - C   2 - A   3 - E   4 - J
5 - B   6 - I   7 - G   8 - H
9 - D   10 - F

Puzzle 98
UMBRELLAS
32

Puzzle 99
THE SEQUENCE
There should be a small
grey umbrella and a small
black umbrella in the
seventh line after the
big black umbrella.
The sequence is made
up of 14 umbrellas: 1 black,
1 grey, 2 black, 1 grey, 3 black,
1 grey, 4 black, 1 grey.
There is 1 large umbrella
every 10 umbrellas.

Puzzle 100
NUMBER SQUARE

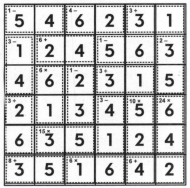

5	4	6	2	3	1
1	2	4	5	6	3
4	6	2	3	1	5
2	1	3	4	5	6
6	3	5	1	2	4
3	5	1	6	4	2

Use this page to work out your answers

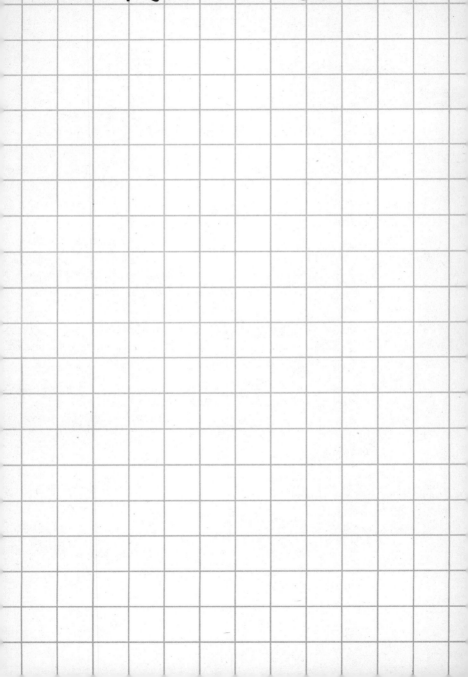

Use this page to work out your answers

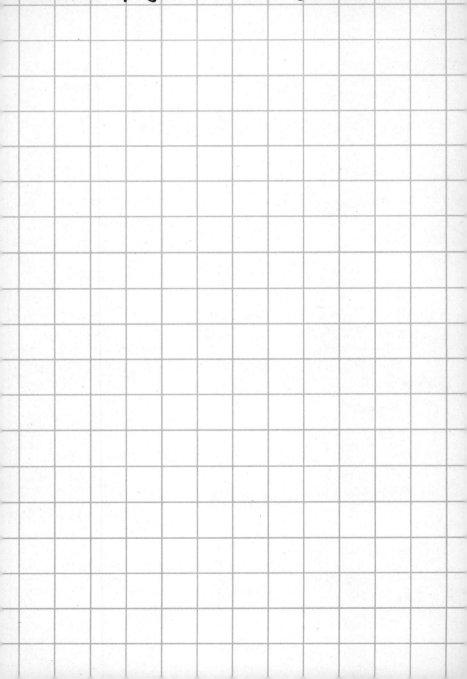

Use this page to work out your answers

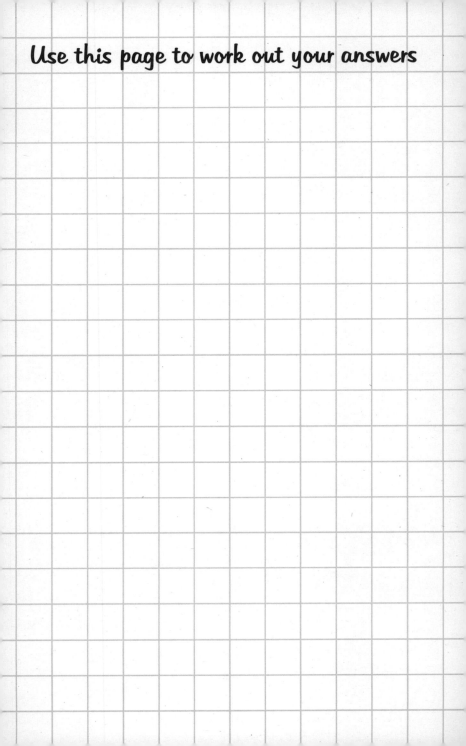

Use this page to work out your answers

Use this page to work out your answers

Use this page to work out your answers

Use this page to work out your answers

Use this page to work out your answers

Use this page to work out your answers

Use this page to work out your answers